D0297449

Handwritten Notes to My Lover

Handwritten Notes to My Lover

hardie grant books
MELBOURNE • LONDON

in assocation with PQ Blackwell

GUESS WHAT?
I LOVE YOU

It's true
I can't keep it a secret
from you any longer
I LOVE YOU!

You make my heart sing!

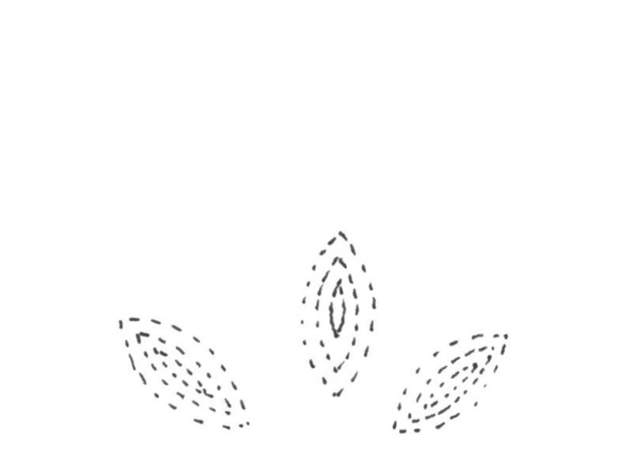

there are people who one loves
immediately and forever.
you are one of those people.

I Began to write a poem
to tell you how I feel
but everything just came out in a
string of humdrum clichés and
bad rhymes
In the end, all I really want to say is
If you want me I'm yours

I Love You

IT'S TRUE, I HAVE A
CRUSH ON YOU...
WHEN YOU'RE AROUND I CAN'T CONCENTRATE.
I WOULDN'T EVEN BE ABLE TO FOCUS
LONG ENOUGH TO WRITE THIS NOTE.

IT'S YOU
I CHOOSE

You complete Me

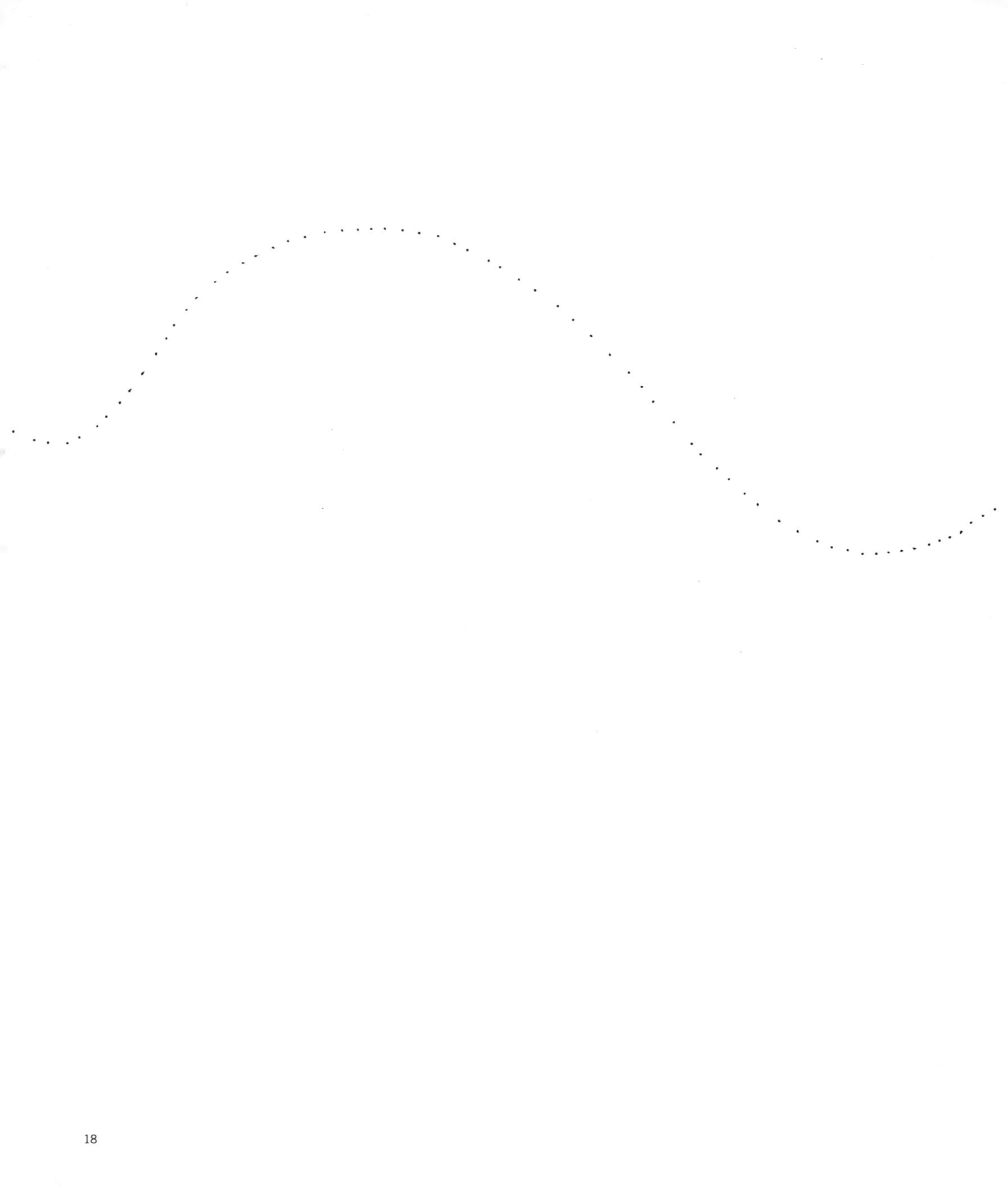

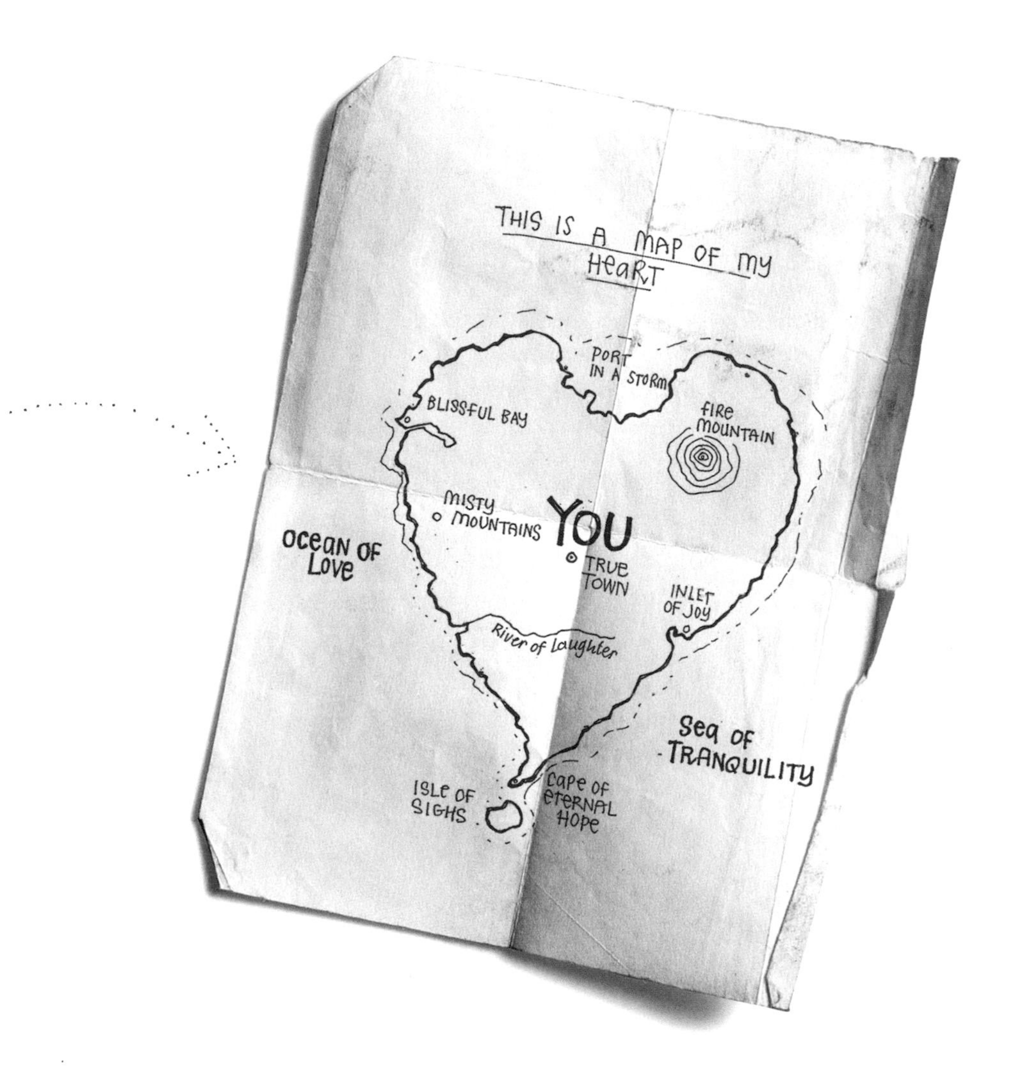
THIS IS A MAP OF MY HEART
PORT IN A STORM
BLISSFUL BAY
FIRE MOUNTAIN
MISTY MOUNTAINS
YOU
TRUE TOWN
OCEAN OF LOVE
INLET OF JOY
River of Laughter
Sea OF TRANQUILITY
ISLE OF SIGHS
CAPE OF ETERNAL HOPE

as for love ...
it is an anchor for me
keeps me warm and brave
when the going gets tough

[ME] − [YOU] = [LONELY & BLUE]

(missing you)

I AM COMPLETELY LOVESICK
PLEASE COME AND MOP MY FEVERED BROW

Love me
Love me NOT
Love me
Love me NOT
Love me
Love me NOT
Love me
Love me NOT
Love me
Love me NOT
Love me
Love me not
Love me
Love me NOT
Love me
Love me NOT
Love me
Love me NOT
Love me
Love me NOT
Love me
You love me?

I'm all
askew
without
you

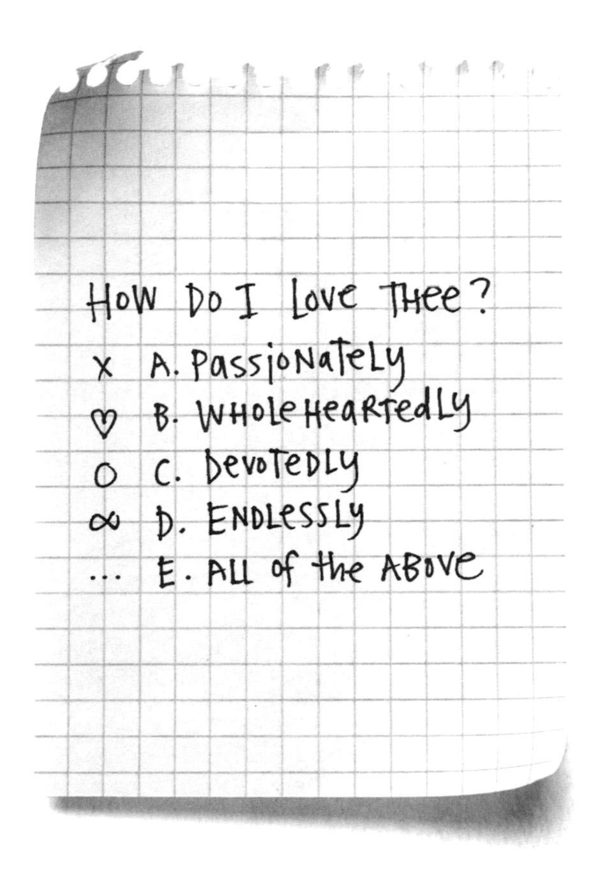
HOW DO I LOVE THEE?
x A. PASSIONATELY
♡ B. WHOLEHEARTEDLY
O C. DEVOTEDLY
∞ D. ENDLESSLY
... E. ALL of the ABOVE

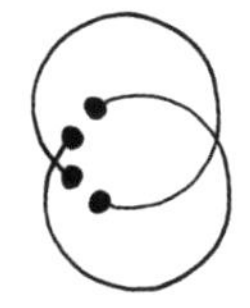

CREAM
NOTE PAPER
HUNDRED SHEETS
from the moment we met,
I knew you were
THE ONE.

REMEMBER
OUR FIRST
KISS

JUST WHAT WERE YOU THINKING
KISSING ME LIKE THAT!
YOU'VE GOT A NERVE.
NOW I'M ALL AQUIVER...
COME BACK AND DO IT AGAIN.

WHEN YOU ARE GONE
YOUR SCENT LINGERS...
IT'S LIKE YOU – ELUSIVE,
INDESCRIBABLE...
IF ONLY I
COULD
BOTTLE
IT.
EAU DE
YOU

Once in a while,
right in the middle
of an ordinary life,
Love gives us
a fairy tale.

NEWSFLASH
I LOVE YOU

DID YOU KNOW that if you silently mouth the word "colourful" it looks exactly like "I LOVE YOU"

COLOURFUL COLOURFUL
COLOURFUL COLOURFUL
COLOURFUL COLOURFUL COLOURFUL
COLOURFUL COLOURFUL COLOURFUL
COLOURFUL COLOURFUL
COLOURFUL COLOURFUL
COLOURFUL COLOURFUL
COLOURFUL COLOURFUL
COLOURFUL
(colourful)

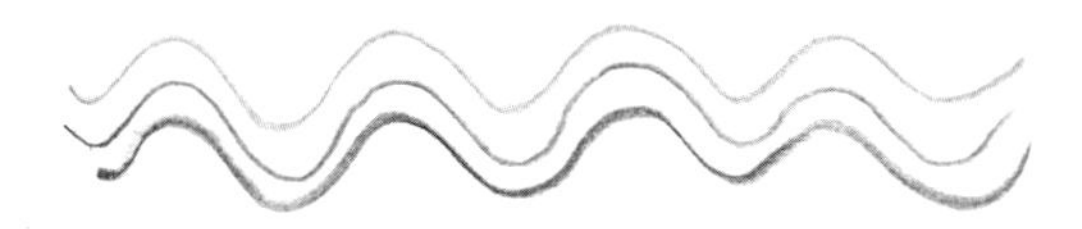

I WANT TO SEE YOU.
MEET ME AT THE
KISSING
PLACE.

66929
66929
MEETING YOU
WAS A
DIVINE
ACCIDENT

YOU'RE THE BEE'S KNEES
(BEES HAVE AMAZING KNEES)

I love you.
You are poetry and
butterflies and
rice pudding

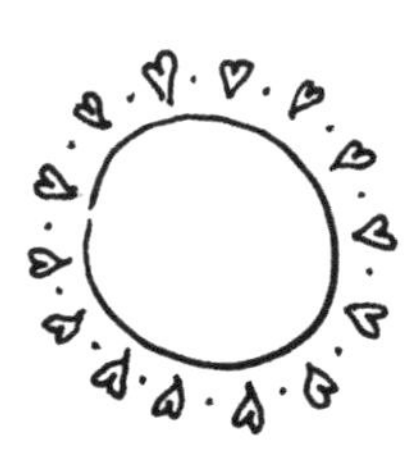

You're a fabulous, Beautiful, unique and Brilliant person.

I thought you should know
that lately even the most ordinary
things (like buying the groceries!)
give me enjoyment.
I love having you in my life.
You make me happy.

LIST OF POSSIBLE ENDEARMENTS I AM CONSIDERING FOR YOU. PLEASE CIRCLE THE ONES THAT APPEAL.

- ANGEL-FACE
- BABY
- BABY-KINS
- BOO
- BUNNY-HEART
- BUTTERCUP
- CRUMPET
- CUPCAKE
- CUTIE-PATOOTIE
- DARLING
- DEAR HEART
- DOLL-FACE
- DREAMBOAT
- GORGEOUS
- HONEY-PIE
- HOT STUFF
- KITTEN
- LAMBKINS
- LOVE-BUG
- LOVER
- MAIN SQUEEZE
- PEACHES
- POOKY
- QUEEN OF MY HEART
- SUGAR-BRITCHES
- SUGAR-LIPS
- SWEETHEART
- TOOTSIE-WOOTSIE
- TWINKLES

THINGS TO DO

LAUNDRY
GROCERY SHOPPING
PAY POWER BILL
BOOK TICKETS TO SHOW
LOVE YOU EVERY SINGLE MINUTE,
EVERY SINGLE DAY.

one of
my favourite
things:
falling asleep with
you in my arms,
listening to the rain.

I'm confused. I've heard people refer to the unrestrained passion and mutual adoration couples feel for one another early on in a relationship as the 'honeymoon period'.
If that is the case, how long is this honeymoon period meant to last? Is there an average timeframe? I don't know about you, but I feel like ours has never ended.
Every single day I love you more.

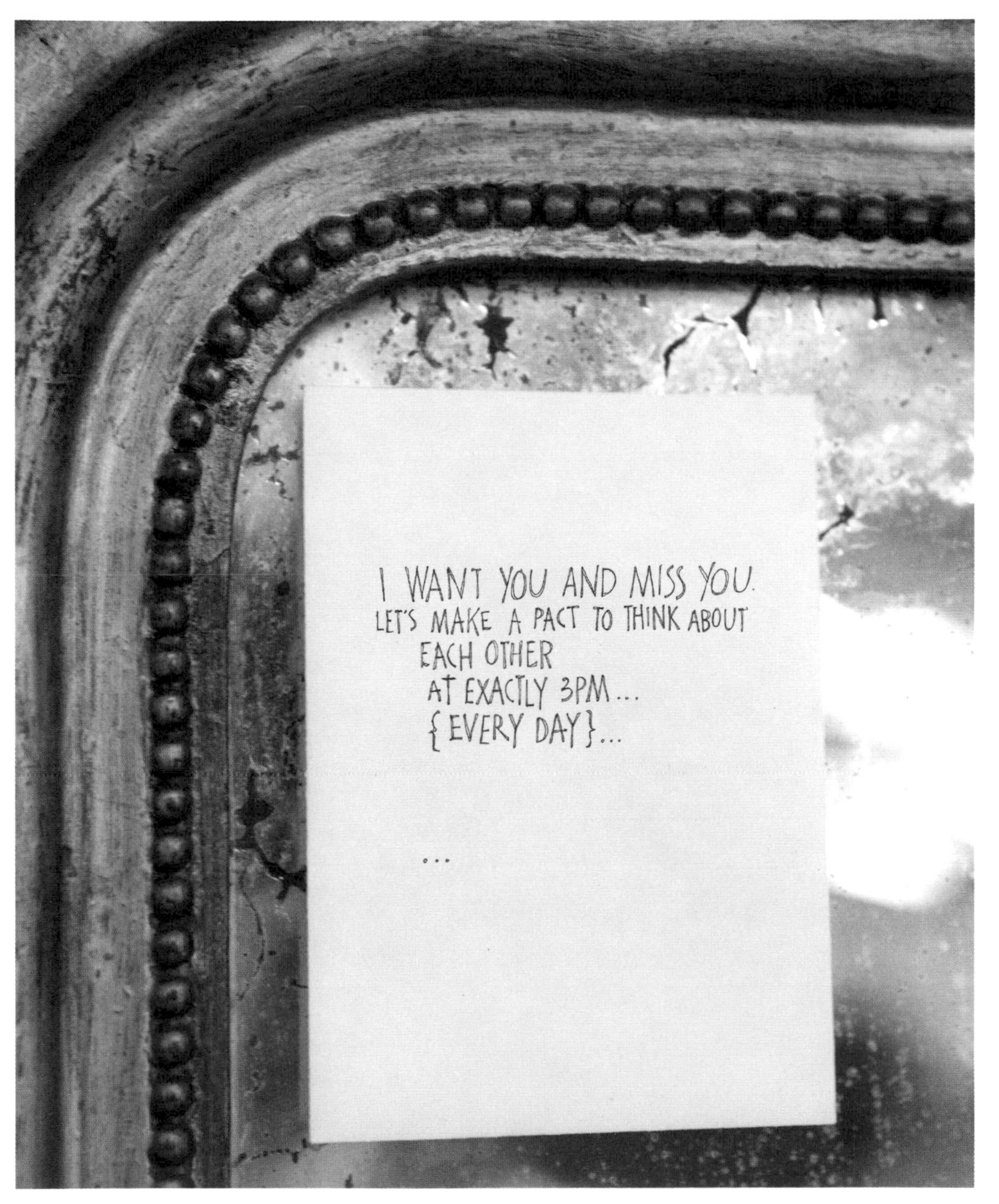
I WANT YOU AND MISS YOU.
LET'S MAKE A PACT TO THINK ABOUT
EACH OTHER
AT EXACTLY 3PM...
{EVERY DAY}...
...

ME 4 YOU

THE WORLD IS A BIG PLACE
AND I HAVE SEEN
SOME WONDERFUL THINGS,
BUT YOUR ARMS ARE
STILL MY FAVOURITE
PLACE TO BE.

x x x

if I never met you
I wouldn't like you
if I didn't like you
I wouldn't love you
If I didn't love you
I wouldn't miss you
But I did, I do, and
I will x

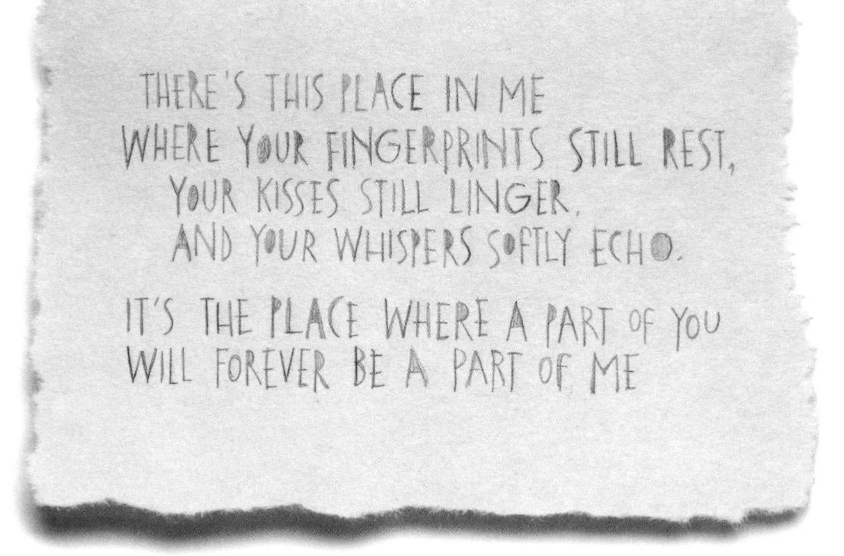
THERE'S THIS PLACE IN ME
WHERE YOUR FINGERPRINTS STILL REST,
YOUR KISSES STILL LINGER,
AND YOUR WHISPERS SOFTLY ECHO.
IT'S THE PLACE WHERE A PART OF YOU
WILL FOREVER BE A PART OF ME

You are my SOULMATE
and I hope that you can see
you are and always will be
THE ONLY ONE FOR ME

ISBN 978-1-74270-058-8

Produced and originated by PQ Blackwell Limited
116 Symonds Street, Auckland, New Zealand
www.pqblackwell.com

Published in 2011 by
Hardie Grant Books
85 High Street
Prahran, Victoria 3181, Australia
www.hardiegrant.com.au

Copyright © 2011 PQ Blackwell Limited

Illustrations by Carla Shale
Quote research and creation by Rachel Clare
Book design by Cameron Gibb and Sarah Anderson
Photograph acknowledgements are as follows: pp. 4–5, 9, 23, 27, 31, 32, 41, 47, 53, 59 and 63 by Jacqui Blanchard; pp. 6, 10 (paintbrush and inkwell), 12, 15, 17, 28, 35, 38 (pencils), 44–45 (rice) and 50 by Carla Shale; front and back cover and pp. 10 (ink spots), 11, 16, 19, 21, 25, 29, 34, 37, 38 (tag), 42, 45 (notepaper), 48, 49, 51, 52, 55, 57 and 61 by iStockphoto.

All rights reserved. No part of this publication may be reproduced or transmitted in any form or by any means, electronic or mechanical, including photocopying, recording, or any information storage and retrieval systems, without permission in writing from the publisher.

The publisher is grateful for literary permissions to reproduce items subject to copyright. Every effort has been made to trace the copyright holders and the publisher apologises for any unintentional omission. We would be pleased to hear from any not acknowledged and undertake to make all reasonable efforts to include the appropriate acknowledgement in any subsequent editions.

Printed in China